shadows

CITY EYE

Paul Blum

D0319140

London Borough of Richmond Upon Thames	
CA	
90710 000 006 157	
Askews	
JF	£5.00
	9781846804571

DISCARDED
RICHMOND UPON THAMES
LIBRARY SERVICE

Rising Stars UK Ltd.
22 Grafton Street, London W1S 4EX
www.risingstars-uk.com

nasen
Helping Everyone Achieve
■ ■■ ■■■ **nasen**

NASEN House, 4/5 Amber Business Village, Amber Close,
Amington, Tamworth, Staffordshire B77 4RP

Text © Rising Stars UK Ltd.
The right of Paul Blum to be identified as the author of this work has
been asserted by him in accordance with the Copyright, Design and
Patents Act 1988.

Published 2008

Cover design: pentacor**big**
Illustrator: Chris King, Illustration Ltd.
Text design and typesetting: pentacor**big**
Publisher: Gill Budgell
Editor: Catherine Baker
Editorial project management: Margot O'Keeffe
Editorial consultant: Lorraine Petersen
Photos: Alamy

All rights reserved. No part of this publication may be reproduced, stored
in a retrieval system or transmitted in any form by any means, electronic,
mechanical, photocopying, recording or otherwise without the prior
permission of Rising Stars UK Ltd.

British Library Cataloguing in Publication Data.
A CIP record for this book is available from the British Library.

ISBN: 978-1-84680-457-1

Printed by Craft Print International Limited, Singapore

Contents

The Crash

- The Crash happened in 2021. Alien space ships crash landed on Earth.

- After The Crash, the Earth became very cold and dark.

- Now the aliens rule the world.

- The aliens have changed shape so they look like people.

- People call the aliens The Enemy.

Life after The Crash

- People are afraid.

- They do not know who is an Enemy and who is a friend.

The Firm

- The Firm keeps order on the streets.

- The Firm keeps people safe from Enemy attacks.

About Matt Merton

Matt Merton works for The Firm. He often works with Dexter. Their job is to find and kill The Enemy. They use Truth Sticks to do this.

But Matt has problems.

Matt has lost his memory. He cannot answer some big questions.

- Where has Jane, his girlfriend, gone?

- How did he get his job with The Firm?

Matt thinks The Firm is on the side of good. But is it?

chapter 1

Matt sat in the bar.
'Get me a coffee,' he said.

'With an extra shot?' asked Sam, the bar man.

'Yes, with an extra shot — and make it extra hot,' said Matt. 'I must spend a lot of money in here, Sam.'

'You do spend a lot of money in here. You're my best customer,' said Sam.

Matt's phone rang. It was work.

Matt worked for The Firm.
The Firm was important.

The Firm kept the city safe.

'Where are you going tonight?' asked Sam.

'There is danger on the City Eye, the big wheel in the city,' said Matt. 'I must go now.'

Since The Crash, Matt had worked hard. Since The Crash, attacks on the city came almost every day.

The Enemy was everywhere. They were spreading fear in the city.

Matt went down to the river. There were lots of people.

The sky was grey. It was cold, night and day. It was cold, summer and winter.

Matt knew how to find The Enemy.
He was trained.

He stood by the ticket hall. He watched people
buy tickets for the City Eye.

He looked into their eyes.

Deep into their eyes.

Then he saw the man. His target.

Matt was sure it was him.

chapter 3

Matt followed the man. He got into the same pod.

The ride began.

The pod rose high into the sky.

The man looked nervous. He held a box.

The man kept looking down at the box in his hands.

What was in the box? Was it a bomb?

'Name?' asked Matt. The man did not answer.

'Date of birth?' asked Matt. The man looked the other way.

'Mother's name?' asked Matt.

The man tried to hit Matt.

But Matt was too quick.

He grabbed the box.

Matt smashed the glass pod with the box.

The box fell.
It exploded in the river.

Matt took out his Truth Stick. The people in the pod moved away. They did not want to see or hear.

Matt pointed the Truth Stick at the man.

The man with the bomb was an Enemy. Matt had to kill him. It was his job.

But what did The Enemy want? Was The Enemy 'human'? Was The Enemy 'alien'? Matt did not know. But he wanted to find out.

chapter 4

That night, Matt was back in the bar. It was late.

'Was it a good night's work?' said Sam.

'Yes, it was a good night's work,' said Matt.
'I need a drink. Two shots, extra hot.'

'Two shots, extra hot. Coming right up,' said Sam.

Matt looked out of the window. The street was busy. The people were safe. For now.

about the author

AUTHOR NAME
Paul Blum

JOB
Teacher

LAST KNOWN LOCATION
North London, England

NOTES
Before The Crash taught in Inner–city London
schools. Writer of series of books called
The Extraordinary Files. Believed to be in
hiding from The Firm. Wanted for questioning.
Seems to know more about The Enemy than
he should...